# My Third Monologue Book
## Places NEAR and **FAR**

# My Third Monologue Book

## Places NEAR and FAR

### 102 Monologues for Young Children

by Kristen Dabrowski

MY FIRST ACTING SERIES: VOLUME 3

A SMITH AND KRAUS BOOK • HANOVER, NEW HAMPSHIRE

A Smith and Kraus Book
Published by Smith and Kraus, Inc.
177 Lyme Road, Hanover, NH 03755
www.SmithandKraus.com

First Edition: August 2008
Manufactured in the United States of America
9  8  7  6  5  4  3  2  1

ISBN-13 978-1-57525-602-3 / ISBN-10 1-57525-602-9
Library of Congress Control Number: 2008927864

*To my nephews two:*
*Jack and Drew*

# Contents

Foreword                                          ix

Part 1  Near: Places You Know                      1

Part 2  Near: Places in the United States         39

Part 3  Far: Foreign Countries                    69

Part 4  Far: Imaginary and Far-Out Places        101

# Foreword

Welcome to My First Acting Series! If you are not five to nine years old, PUT DOWN THIS BOOK! (OK, if you are a parent, guardian, teacher, agent, or someone's who's just interested, you are welcome, too.)

In *My First Monologue Book*, we learned about what a monologue is and how to rehearse one. That book covered basic, everyday situations for kids like not wanting to go to bed, having to eat broccoli, and making new friends. If you haven't already seen it, check it out!

Next in the series is *My Second Monologue Book*. This one has situations kids can relate to—interesting places plus famous and historical people. Learn about and pretend to be people from from different times with different lives. It's fun to play new characters!

This book, *My Third Monologue Book*, goes even further. It has everyday situations, but there's a twist. The focus is on where you are. Part 1 is the easiest—normal, everyday places. Parts 2 and 3 are more challenging: they cover places in the United States and the rest of the world. The last section is a lot of fun. It looks at magical, fantastic, and imaginary places.

There's no wrong way to use this book. Dress up, have girls do boys' monologues, write in the book, draw in the book, color the pictures—whatever you like! Feel free to look at maps, check out the Internet, or ask adults and teachers for help with new words and places. (You can peek at the answers on the guessing sections, too, but try to figure it out first!)

See how these books grow with you and your skills? Each book will build on the one before it.

- **Teachers:** Look for the *Teacher's Guide* to this series for many ideas about how to use this book in the classroom.

- **English/Drama Teachers and Parents:** There will also be a guide to acting (*My First Acting Book*) with theater games, exercises, acting techniques, and information on how to be an actor.

- **Agents:** These monologues are immediate and active, with different emotions and levels within each monologue. Great for auditions.

Enjoy and explore!

*Kristen Dabrowski*

# Part 1
# NEAR: PLACES
# YOU KNOW

In this section, you need to play detective. Look for clues in each monologue to figure out where you are! Remember, these are everyday places like a bedroom or a classroom or a store. Answers are on page 37.

Where is this boy? Draw the place around him.

# SUNNY

*Sunny is talking to her brother, Ryan.*

This place is dusty. This isn't fair. I didn't make it dirty up here. Why do I have to clean it?

What's that? Over there! It's moving! It's a ghost!

I'm not going over there. No way! I'm getting out of here!

It's a spider? Oh. Go smush it with your shoe!

---

## CLUEBOOK

Be a detective! Look for clues. Where is Sunny?

CLUE 1: _____

CLUE 2: _____

CLUE 3: _____

CLUE 4: _____

SUNNY: I am in

_____

# ROB

*Rob is talking to his friend, Christopher.*

I forgot—Oh, no! I forgot my gym shorts! I brought them home.

I can't tell the teacher. He'll yell at me! Tell him I'm not in school today. I have to hide so I won't get in trouble!

I'll get in the locker. Just close the door on me. Don't forget to let me out later, OK?

---

**CLUEBOOK**

Be a detective! Look for clues. Where is Rob?

CLUE 1: _____

CLUE 2: _____

CLUE 3: _____

CLUE 4: _____

ROB: I am in

_____

# GINGER

*Ginger is talking to her mother.*

Mom, Dad said he wants cupcakes. Can we get
them?

Oh, Mom, don't put them back. Please? I loooove
cupcakes. Please can we keep them? Pleeeeeease?
I'm not leaving unless you buy them. *(Sits down.)*

Where are you going? Don't leave me!

---

## CLUEBOOK

Be a detective! Look for clues. Where is Ginger?

CLUE 1: _____

CLUE 2: _____

CLUE 3: _____

CLUE 4: _____

GINGER: I am in

_____

# GEORGE

*George is talking to his father.*

I like my hair the way it is. I don't want it cut.
It looks perfect right now.

I know Mom said I have to do it, but I don't want
short hair.

I do not look like a girl! I look like a boy. Don't I?

Well, OK. She can cut off *a little* of my hair. But
that's it!

## CLUEBOOK

Be a detective! Look for clues. Where is George?

CLUE 1: _____

CLUE 2: _____

CLUE 3: _____

CLUE 4: _____

GEORGE: I am in

_____

# JENNY

*Jenny is talking to her brother, Jason, and her mother.*

Hello? Anybody in there? Jason? Jason! You've been in there for hours. I have to go! Hurry up! This is an emergency.

Mom, Jason won't come out. It's an emergency! I have to go. I don't want to go to the one downstairs. The curtains don't close enough. Can't he just leave?

Fine, but I'm not cleaning up if I have an accident running down the stairs!

---

## CLUEBOOK

Be a detective! Look for clues. Where is Jenny?

CLUE 1: _____

CLUE 2: _____

CLUE 3: _____

CLUE 4: _____

JENNY: I am in

_____

# DAVID

*David is talking to his friend, Mike.*

Look at this one! You can make a coin disappear.
Look! Here's a whoopie cushion. You put it down
on a chair, and when someone sits on it, it goes . . .
*(Blows a raspberry.)* I could do that to my sister.

Oh, Mike. Here it is. Here's what I want. A fake
hand. Someone comes to shake your hand and—
ahhh! It comes right off into their hand. They're left
holding this bloody stump.

People shake my hand all the time. I'm getting it.

---

## CLUEBOOK

Be a detective! Look for clues. Where is David?

CLUE 1: _____

CLUE 2: _____

CLUE 3: _____

CLUE 4: _____

DAVID: I am in

_____

# LACEY

*Lacey is talking to her whole family.*

Are you done yet? You've been drinking coffee for hours. I want to go home and watch TV.

Can I try your coffee? Just a little? *(Sips from a coffee cup.)* Yuck! No wonder it takes you so long to drink.

Can we go home now? We've been here so long I'm thirty now.

---

## CLUEBOOK

Be a detective! Look for clues. Where is Lacey?

CLUE 1: _____

CLUE 2: _____

CLUE 3: _____

CLUE 4: _____

LACEY: I am in

_____

# MAX

*Max is talking to a new friend.*

I can't believe you have your own room. I have to share with my brothers. Two of them! They smell.

I'm the youngest, so they always kick me out of my room. I have nowhere to go. I just wander around the house. And I get their leftover toys. Nothing's mine.

You are so lucky. I wish I could come live here.

---

## CLUEBOOK

Be a detective! Look for clues. Where is Max?

CLUE 1: _____

CLUE 2: _____

CLUE 3: _____

CLUE 4: _____

MAX: I am in

_____

# CAROLINE

*Caroline is talking to her sister, Hannah, and her mother.*

The candy? I ate it. Mom said I could!

Mommy, I did not eat *all* of them. I left the ones with the fruit inside. I don't like those. You didn't say I had to wait! You said I could have some!

Hannah, you're such a tattletale. I don't like you.

---

## CLUEBOOK

Be a detective! Look for clues. Where is Caroline?

CLUE 1: _____

CLUE 2: _____

CLUE 3: _____

CLUE 4: _____

CAROLINE: I am in

_____

# RICKY

*Ricky is talking to his grandmother.*

Thanks. A quarter. I'll save it. Promise. I want to buy a bike.

You know, Grandma, bikes are pretty expensive. Um, they cost about a million quarters. So it's gonna take me kind of a long time to get one.

Oh, thanks. Two quarters. I'll put it in my piggybank.

I'm never gonna have a bike.

---

## CLUEBOOK

Be a detective! Look for clues. Where is Ricky?

CLUE 1: _____

CLUE 2: _____

CLUE 3: _____

CLUE 4: _____

RICKY: I am in

_____

# CHARLOTTE

*Charlotte is talking to her father.*

Dad, I can't sleep here. The ground is bumpy and hard, and there are bugs. I don't want to go to the bathroom behind a bush, either.

And . . . I'm . . . scared. It's dark and there are all these noises, and I keep thinking about Hansel and Gretel. You won't leave us here, will you? I know you won't, it's just that . . .

What was that noise? Do owls eat people, Dad?

---

## CLUEBOOK

Be a detective! Look for clues. Where is Charlotte?

CLUE 1: _____

CLUE 2: _____

CLUE 3: _____

CLUE 4: _____

CHARLOTTE: I am in

_____

# GRAHAM

*Graham is talking to a vendor selling ice cream.*

Excuse me, but I dropped my ice cream. It fell.
Can I get a new one?

Why not? I didn't get to eat it.

My mom can't buy me a new one. She's waiting for
me on the boardwalk.

It's got sand on it, mister!

Well . . . I guess it's better than nothing . . . (*Bends
down, picks the ice cream up off the ground, and
licks it.*) It's kind of gritty.

---

## CLUEBOOK

Be a detective! Look for clues. Where is Graham?

CLUE 1: _____

CLUE 2: _____

CLUE 3: _____

CLUE 4: _____

GRAHAM: I am in

_____

---

# ALEXANDRA

*Alexandra is talking to her teacher, Mrs. Epstein.*

*(Her head is tilted to the side.)* Mrs. Epstein—help! Help! The llama—it's eating my hair!

*(Head straight, breathing deeply.)* Is it OK? *(Touches her hair.)* It's wet! Ew! Are both sides still even? Is one shorter than the other?

Stop laughing at me, you guys! It's not funny. It's gross!

---

## CLUEBOOK

Be a detective! Look for clues. Where is Alexandra?

CLUE 1: _____

CLUE 2: _____

CLUE 3: _____

CLUE 4: _____

ALEXANDRA: I am in

_____

# CHARLIE

*Charlie is talking to a guy selling tickets.*
*He's with his friend Frank.*

Three tickets for *Death Smash*, please. My dad is with us. He's just over there. There. That guy with the cane. That's my dad. He said it's OK for us to see this movie.

Well, yeah, he's kind of old. But you shouldn't say that. It's not polite.

Awesome! We got tickets to *Death Smash*, Frank!

Hi, Mom. We bought the tickets. No, Mom, we're not seeing *Buddy and Me*. We're seeing *Death Smash*! But, Mom, we already got the tickets!

---

## CLUEBOOK

Be a detective! Look for clues. Where is Charlie?

CLUE 1: _____

CLUE 2: _____

CLUE 3: _____

CLUE 4: _____

CHARLIE: I am in

_____

---

# SYDNEY

*Sydney is talking to her little sister, Grace.*

We are going to make a cake for Mom's birthday, Grace. I saw the box in the cupboard. We'll surprise her. When she wakes up, we'll have a cake all ready for her!

OK, you get the eggs, and I'll get the sugar. Of course I know how to do this! I've watched Mom do it a million times. You break the eggs and put them—Grace, you don't throw broken eggs in the bowl! You can't put the egg shells in a cake! Now the cake will be crunchy. Well, it's too late now. Maybe they'll melt in the oven. I hope Mom likes this!

---

## CLUEBOOK

Be a detective! Look for clues. Where is Sydney?

CLUE 1: _____

CLUE 2: _____

CLUE 3: _____

CLUE 4: _____

SYDNEY: I am in

_____

# MALCOLM

*Malcolm is sitting on a table, talking to a nurse.*

I feel fine. My head hurts a little. I was jumping off of the sofa. We don't have a trampoline. So I use the sofa as a trampoline. It doesn't work very well.

My friend Ben has a trampoline. I ask for one every Christmas, but my mom says I'll hurt myself if I get one.

Do you think you could tell her to give me one? I mean, I already got hurt. At least with a trampoline no one's going to put a pointy table next to it.

---

## CLUEBOOK

Be a detective! Look for clues. Where is Malcolm?

CLUE 1: _____

CLUE 2: _____

CLUE 3: _____

CLUE 4: _____

MALCOLM: I am in

_____

---

# RACHEL

*Rachel is sitting in a chair with her legs stretched in front of her.*

But that's impossible. I brush every day. Every day! I swear! OK, once my mom told me to get up, but I didn't get up, I stayed in bed, then she came up again and said, "Hurry up, we're going out for pancakes." Well, I love pancakes so I hurried up, and I didn't brush my teeth. That one day. Can your teeth rot in just one day?

So just 'cause I didn't brush my teeth that Saturday I have a cavity? Do pancakes make you have cavities?

You can get cavities even if you brush your teeth every single day? Then why bother?

---

## CLUEBOOK

Be a detective! Look for clues. Where is Rachel?

CLUE 1: _____

CLUE 2: _____

CLUE 3: _____

CLUE 4: _____

RACHEL: I am in

_____

---

# WILL

*Will is talking to his dad.*

How many can I take out? Can I get this one? I'll read it. I promise! It's about space. It says here that a black hole—

What? Nobody's even here. We're the only ones here, Dad. I'm not bothering anybody. Well, I can be quiet, but nobody's here—Fine. I'll keep my voice down.

Some rules don't make any sense to me. I'm not being smart. I'm just saying . . .

So can I get this book?

---

**CLUEBOOK**

Be a detective! Look for clues. Where is Will?

CLUE 1: _____

CLUE 2: _____

CLUE 3: _____

CLUE 4: _____

WILL: I am in

_____

---

# GILLIAN

*Gillian is talking to her mother.*

I want to make sure this gets to the North Pole. How many stamps do I need? One? Are you sure? Just one? Can we put two on, just in case? And the address is OK? Santa Claus, North Pole. That's enough. You're absolutely, positively sure?

OK. I just really want to get the Gretchen doll for Christmas. She's so pretty, Mom. So Santa has to get this letter.

Thank you for driving me here. I like Mailman Bob, but I thought he might drop my letter on the way here . . . I just have to make sure my list gets to Santa!

---

## CLUEBOOK

Be a detective! Look for clues. Where is Gillian?

CLUE 1: _____

CLUE 2: _____

CLUE 3: _____

CLUE 4: _____

GILLIAN: I am in

_____

---

# STEVEN

*Steven is sitting, talking to his mother.*

I don't feel so good. Mom? It's just that it's so bumpy. Yeah, I have my seatbelt on. It's my . . . stomach. I might . . . throw up.

No, I don't want to hold a bag. I don't know. No one else is. I'll look stupid. I'll be fine. I just don't feel good. Are we almost there?

We'll be landing soon? No, I'm OK. I can make it. Ooooooooh. I'm fine, Mom! Ooooooooh. Where's that barf bag?!

---

## CLUEBOOK

Be a detective! Look for clues. Where is Steven?

CLUE 1: _____

CLUE 2: _____

CLUE 3: _____

CLUE 4: _____

STEVEN: I am in

_____

# VANESSA

*Vanessa is sitting in a chair, waiting for Mr. Griswold to come in.*

I didn't do anything wrong. I don't know why I'm in trouble. *He* was bothering *me*!

Mr. Griswold, please don't call my mom and dad. It wasn't my fault! He was pulling my hair! I know I shouldn't have hit him, but he kept bugging me. Please don't call my parents! I promise I won't ever do it again.

You *have* to call them? But Billy started it!

---

## CLUEBOOK

Be a detective! Look for clues. Where is Vanessa?

CLUE 1: _____

CLUE 2: _____

CLUE 3: _____

CLUE 4: _____

VANESSA: I am in

_____

---

# BRENDAN

*Brendan is talking to his mother.*

Do I have to try them on? Can I do it at home? I bet they're fine. They look fine.

I don't know. I don't like trying things on. It takes too long. I don't like coming out of the dressing room and showing you. I don't know . . . It's embarrassing. There are other people there looking. And you say stuff like, "Oh, that looks cute on you, Brendan! Turn around, let me see your tushie." Mom, I really wish you wouldn't say tushie.

Can we just go home now? Aw, all right. I'll try on the pants.

---

## CLUEBOOK

Be a detective! Look for clues. Where is Brendan?

CLUE 1: _____

CLUE 2: _____

CLUE 3: _____

CLUE 4: _____

BRENDAN: I am in

_____

---

# ANNIE

*Annie is playing with her friends Lucy and Jeanette.*

OK, we're going to race from the jungle gym to that tree over there. But—Wait, Jeanette! I didn't say go! There are more rules! OK, you're a baby, Jeanette; and you're three years old, Lucy; and I'm your mother. So you both have to run like little kids. Well, Lucy, you run like a little kid, and Jeanette, you run like a baby. So maybe you shouldn't even run. Maybe you should crawl.

Where are you going? You want to play on the swings instead? OK, but you two are the parents, and I'm the little kid, so you have to push me, OK?

---

**CLUEBOOK**

Be a detective! Look for clues. Where is Annie?

CLUE 1: _____

CLUE 2: _____

CLUE 3: _____

CLUE 4: _____

ANNIE: I am in

_____

---

# TJ

*TJ is talking to his friend, Brian.*

We've been walking for a long time. I thought this was a short cut, but . . . I don't even see the path anymore. I can't see the street, either! We're lost, Brian. I don't know if we'll ever get home.

I'm sorry. I thought I knew where I was going. I can't help it! All the trees look the same. I don't know what to do now. We just have to keep walking. We'll be OK, Brian.

It sure is getting dark . . .

## CLUEBOOK

Be a detective! Look for clues. Where is TJ?

CLUE 1: _____

CLUE 2: _____

CLUE 3: _____

CLUE 4: _____

TJ: I am in

_____

# LAURA

*Laura is talking to a woman behind a desk.*

Excuse me, ma'am? Where can I go to open an account? I have my all my birthday money here, and I want to leave it here for safekeeping.

It's not enough to open an savings account? This is all of my money from my whole life! How much money do I need? Fifty dollars? But I only have ten dollars and forty-seven cents!

I guess I'll be back in forty years.

---

## CLUEBOOK

Be a detective! Look for clues. Where is Laura?

CLUE 1: _____

CLUE 2: _____

CLUE 3: _____

CLUE 4: _____

LAURA: I am in

_____

# MATT

*Matt is talking to his sister.*

You got salt in your eye? Well, duh. No! Don't tell Mom you want to go home. Because I don't want to go home. I'm having fun! It's not fair.

There are some big waves out today! The sun is shining, too. It's not too cold. I don't care if there's sand in my bathing suit, I want to stay here until it's dark. I'm not ready to go home yet!

---

## CLUEBOOK

Be a detective! Look for clues. Where is Matt?

CLUE 1: _____

CLUE 2: _____

CLUE 3: _____

CLUE 4: _____

MATT: I am in

_____

# HARMONY

*Harmony is talking to her mother.*

Mom, these ones aren't very pretty. I know they're good for school, but I wish . . . I wish I could get really pretty ones to wear to school. Like the shiny ones with the buckle on the sides.

I won't ruin them! I love them. I'd be so careful. I would watch each and every step I make so I don't scuff them up.

I hate being practical! I don't want to wear these boring old sneakers to school!

---

### CLUEBOOK

Be a detective! Look for clues. Where is Harmony?

CLUE 1: _____

CLUE 2: _____

CLUE 3: _____

CLUE 4: _____

HARMONY: I am in

_____

# SIMON

*Simon is talking to his father.*

That's the biggest TV I ever saw! Can we get that one? That's as big as a movie screen!

I saw a video camera here, too. Can we get one so we can make movies? I want to make one about pirates.

We're here to get a regular old camera? Why do people take pictures anyway? They're boring. They help you remember things when you're old? I'm not going to get old, so let's get the big TV instead.

---

## CLUEBOOK

Be a detective! Look for clues. Where is Simon?

CLUE 1: _____

CLUE 2: _____

CLUE 3: _____

CLUE 4: _____

SIMON: I am in

_____

# RENEE

*Renee is talking to her mother and her brother, Joey.*

Mom, Joey splashed me again. And the water went up my nose. And he said he's not sorry. He said I'm not allowed in the deep end because I'm too little, and he owns it. I told him he can't own the pool, and he says he called it first. So can you tell him that he's in trouble and he doesn't own the pool, and he's not allowed to splash me?

Be quiet, Joey, I am not a tattletale. You're a bad boy, and I don't like you!

---

**CLUEBOOK**

Be a detective! Look for clues. Where is Renee?

CLUE 1: _____

CLUE 2: _____

CLUE 3: _____

CLUE 4: _____

RENEE: I am in

_____

---

# BILL

*Bill is talking to his friend.*

*(Looking up.)* What shapes do you see? I see a rabbit. Over there!

Corn, corn everywhere you look. Dad says he's going to cut down the corn in a few weeks. Then we'll have corn bread, corn fritters, corn on the cob . . . Most of it we'll sell, though. Can you imagine eating all this corn? It's like a forest.

When I grow up, I'm going to be so tall that I'll be able to see over the corn. I will! You'll see.

---

## CLUEBOOK

Be a detective! Look for clues. Where is Bill?

CLUE 1: _____

CLUE 2: _____

CLUE 3: _____

CLUE 4: _____

BILL: I am in

_____

---

# ZOE

*Zoe is talking to her mother.*

Mommy, I don't want to go to school. I don't feel so good. My stomach hurts. And I'm dizzy. Can I stay home today?

I just don't feel so good. No, I don't want breakfast. I'm not hungry. I just want to lie in bed. Can I just go back to sleep?

Thank you, Mommy. I love you.

---

## CLUEBOOK

Be a detective! Look for clues. Where is Zoe?

CLUE 1: _____

CLUE 2: _____

CLUE 3: _____

CLUE 4: _____

ZOE: I am in

_____

# ALEX

*Alex is talking to his mother.*

Round and round and round and round. I get dizzy looking at this thing. How many quarters do we have left? I'm sorry I put too much detergent in the last load.

This place is boring. Why can't we go somewhere else? Who wants to steal someone else's wet or dirty clothes?

Fine. How much longer do we have to wait? Oh nooooo! This is torture!

---

## CLUEBOOK

Be a detective! Look for clues. Where is Alex?

CLUE 1: _____

CLUE 2: _____

CLUE 3: _____

CLUE 4: _____

ALEX: I am in

_____

# EVE

*Eve is talking to a man behind a counter.*

May I have a cheese sandwich, please? No, I don't want ham. No, I don't want tomatoes. Just cheese on a roll.

That's all I like! My brother only eats steak and hamburgers. We're the opposite. No, I don't just eat cheese. I also eat peanut butter and spaghetti. I'm a vegetarian.

My mom says it's not nice for me to tell people not to eat animals. So how come everybody is allowed to tell me I should eat meat?

---

## CLUEBOOK

Be a detective! Look for clues. Where is Eve?

CLUE 1: _____

CLUE 2: _____

CLUE 3: _____

CLUE 4: _____

EVE: I am in

_____

---

# HOWIE

*Howie is talking to his mother.*

Mom, I like this chair. You don't like anything I pick! Isn't this supposed to be my room? How do you know what I'll like when I'm older? I bet I'll still like race cars and tigers. I bet I'll like those things the rest of my life!

You made me come here because you said I had to help you pick stuff. You're not letting me pick anything! I didn't get to pick the bed or the rug or the chair or anything!

I hate being a kid.

---

### CLUEBOOK

Be a detective! Look for clues. Where is Howie?

CLUE 1: _____

CLUE 2: _____

CLUE 3: _____

CLUE 4: _____

HOWIE: I am in

_____

# MARGOT

*Margot is talking to her teacher.*

How old is this painting? Why do people like it?
The eyes aren't even in the right place. I think I
could do one like this. I also have a question about
the painting in the other room. It looks like the
man spilled his paint. Did he make it like that on
purpose?

I don't think I understand art. I like math better.

---

**CLUEBOOK**

Be a detective! Look for clues. Where is Margot?

CLUE 1: _____

CLUE 2: _____

CLUE 3: _____

CLUE 4: _____

MARGOT: I am in

_____

---

# ANSWERS!

| | |
|---|---|
| Sunny is in | the attic. |
| Rob is in | the locker room at school. |
| Ginger is in | the grocery store. |
| George is in | a barbershop. |
| Jenny is outside | the bathroom. |
| David is in | a magic shop. |
| Lacey is in | a restaurant (or coffee shop). |
| Max is in | his friend's bedroom. |
| Caroline is in | in a candy store. |
| Ricky is at | his grandmother's house. |
| Charlotte is at | a camp ground. |
| Graham is in | an ice cream shop on the beach. |
| Alexandra is at | the zoo. |
| Charlie is in front of | a movie theater. |
| Sydney is in | the kitchen. |
| Malcolm is in | the hospital (or a doctor's office). |
| Rachel is at | the dentist. |
| Will is in | the library. |
| Gillian is in | the post office. |
| Steven is on | an airplane. |
| Vanessa is in | the principal's office. |

Brendan is in          a clothing store.

Annie is in            a park/playground.

TJ is in               the woods.

Laura is at            the bank.

Matt is in             the ocean.

Harmony is in          the shoe store.

Simon is in            the electronics store.

Renee is in            a pool.

Bill is in             a cornfield.

Zoe is in              bed (in her bedroom).

Alex is in             a laundromat.

Eve is                 in a deli.

Howie is in            a furniture store.

Margot is in           a museum.

# Part 2
# NEAR: PLACES IN
# THE UNITED STATES

In this section, each character is in a place in the United States. On the next page is a list of cities and states: Match a city and state to each monologue. You may need to go on the Internet or look on a map for help. Answers are on page 66.

Where is this girl? Draw the place around her.

## Match a city and state from the list below to each monologue.

Tahlequah, Oklahoma

Denver, Colorado

Honolulu, Hawaii

Flagstaff, Arizona

Fort Lauderdale, Florida

Nantucket, Massachusetts

Boston, Massachusetts

Nashville, Tennessee

Las Vegas, Nevada

Louisville, Kentucky

Washington, D.C.

Keystone, South Dakota

Detroit, Michigan

Salt Lake City, Utah

New Orleans, Louisiana

Chicago, Illinois

Atlanta, Georgia

San Francisco Bay, California

Point Pleasant, New Jersey

New York, New York

Los Angeles, California

Anchorage, Alaska

Laredo, Texas

Philadelphia, Pennsylvania

Williamsburg, Virginia

# LEAH

*Leah is talking to her teacher.*

*(Running into the room.)* Mrs. Nunez, I'm sorry I'm late for school. My mom told me to tell you that we got stuck in traffic on the freeway. But that's not true. She got a call from her agent in Hollywood about an audition for a movie, so she had to change her clothes before she drove me to school. She's an actress.

OK, I'll sit down, but I have to tell you one more thing. My next door neighbor is on a TV show. That's it.

---

### PRIVATE EYE NOTEBOOK

1. Circle clues about the *weather*.
2. Underline *facts* about the city or state.
3. Put a star next to *proper* nouns.
4. Why is this place famous or important?

NOTES: _____

_____

LEAH: I am in

_____

# IAIN

*Ian is talking to his father.*

Do you think we'll see the president while we're here? I hope so. Then I can tell him that we think he's stupid. And then I'll ask him why there needs to be war. I can't wait to see what he says.

He's here? Now? Where? *(Looks to the left. Stands still and stares, shocked.)* There he is! Dad! *(Excited.)* The president!

Dad, we saw the president of the United States! For a second! Oh, no. I forgot to ask him my questions!

---

## PRIVATE EYE NOTEBOOK

1. Circle clues about the *weather*.
2. Underline *facts* about the city or state.
3. Put a star next to *proper* nouns.
4. Why is this place famous or important?

NOTES: _____

_____

IAIN: I am in

_____

# JODIE

*Jodie is talking to her brother and sister.*

What are we going to do? We can't get to school!
I'm not going out there with that moose right
outside the door. Moose are mean! We just have to
wait. But I'm going to get in trouble. Why do there
have to be moose in the world?

We should just move to somewhere warm.
Somewhere without snow and moose and eskimos.
We were going to play with a parachute in gym
class, and Claire was going to bring in cupcakes for
her birthday. I want to go to school. Go away,
moose!

---

## PRIVATE EYE NOTEBOOK

1. Circle clues about the *weather*.
2. Underline *facts* about the city or state.
3. Put a star next to *proper* nouns.
4. Why is this place famous or important?

NOTES: _____

_____

JODIE: I am in

_____

# RICH

*Rich is talking to his father.*

Motor City? This looks like everywhere else. I thought since this is the automobile capital that the cars would be different. Better.

Motor City and Motown are the same place? So this city is famous for cars and music? Not every city is famous for two things! People who live here must be pretty smart.

---

## PRIVATE EYE NOTEBOOK

1. Circle clues about the *weather*.
2. Underline *facts* about the city or state.
3. Put a star next to *proper* nouns.
4. Why is this place famous or important?

NOTES: _____

_____

RICH: I am in

_____

---

# LAILA

*Laila is talking to her teacher, Mrs. Kona.*

Wait a minute. This whole island is made of lava from a volcano? How come there's grass? How come it's not hot? How come I never knew this? That's so weird!

The island is growing all the time? How? Because there are still volcanoes erupting? Eeek!

So, Mrs. Kona, should we move or something? Is it safe to live here?

---

### PRIVATE EYE NOTEBOOK

1. Circle clues about the *weather*.
2. Underline *facts* about the city or state.
3. Put a star next to *proper* nouns.
4. Why is this place famous or important?

NOTES: _____

_____

LAILA: I am in

_____

# CHRISTIAN

*Christian is talking to his father.*

Can we ride our horses to Mexico? I just learned in school that we live next to a whole other country! Why didn't you tell me that? People speak Spanish in Mexico, right? Can you speak Spanish?

We're the biggest state, right? Alaska is bigger than here?

Are there cowboys here? I ask a lot of questions? You think so?

---

### PRIVATE EYE NOTEBOOK

1. Circle clues about the *weather*.
2. Underline *facts* about the city or state.
3. Put a star next to *proper* nouns.
4. Why is this place famous or important?

NOTES: _____

_____

CHRISTIAN: I am in

_____

# JAZMEEN

*Jazmeen is talking to the new girl in school.*

You're new? It's nice here. I guess it's loud. There's a lot of people and a lot of traffic. I've lived in the city my whole life. I was born here.

You can come to my apartment after school, if you want. I live one subway stop away, at 135th Street, but we can walk. My mom will still be at work—she sells tickets at a Broadway theater—so we can watch cartoons. My brother might be home, but we don't have to pay any attention to him. He just sits on the couch and text-messages his friends. He's boring.

---

## PRIVATE EYE NOTEBOOK

1. Circle clues about the *weather*.
2. Underline *facts* about the city or state.
3. Put a star next to *proper* nouns.
4. Why is this place famous or important?

NOTES: _____

_____

JAZMEEN: I am in

_____

# THOMAS

*Thomas is talking to a stranger. The year is 1693.*

You want to go to sea? You came to the right place. All of the whaling ships leave from here.

Are you running from something? Most people go to sea to escape something. It's a lonely life out there in the middle of the ocean. Dangerous, too.

Where are you from? Salem? Isn't that where they have all those witches? Don't worry, mister. I'll keep your secret.

---

## PRIVATE EYE NOTEBOOK

1. Circle clues about the *weather*.
2. Underline *facts* about the city or state.
3. Put a star next to *proper* nouns.
4. Why is this place famous or important?

NOTES: _____

_____

THOMAS: I am in

_____

# IRIS

*Iris is talking to her friend Maria.*

*Hola*, chicka, how you doin'? It's scorchin' out here in the sun. Wanna go to the beach? My dad gave me money, and my sister's gonna take us. We can grab a taco while she's showing off in her bikini. I know, it's gross! But we need to go to the beach before the spring-break kids come. Then my dad won't let me go. He says the college kids act loco.

When I go to college, I'm going to study, not party. So I'll get straight As. So I can be a doctor. Who cares about boys? They're yucky. Then I'll open a nightclub so I can dance all night.

---

### PRIVATE EYE NOTEBOOK

1. Circle clues about the *weather*.
2. Underline *facts* about the city or state.
3. Put a star next to *proper* nouns.
4. Why is this place famous or important?

NOTES: _____

_____

IRIS: I am in

_____

# JAY

*Jay is talking to a tour guide.*

This is the tallest building in the whole United States? No way! We're going to go to the top? Wait a minute. Mom?

I don't know if I want to do this. It's a windy day, Mom! Don't they call this the Windy City? And this is the tallest building in the United States. What if— What if it blows over?

Are you sure nothing will happen? Well . . . I guess I'll go. But hold my hand, OK?

---

### PRIVATE EYE NOTEBOOK

1. Circle clues about the *weather*.
2. Underline *facts* about the city or state.
3. Put a star next to *proper* nouns.
4. Why is this place famous or important?

NOTES: _____

_____

JAY: I am in

_____

---

# DOMINIQUE

*Dominique is talking to her mother in the car.*

Mom, why did Hurricane Katrina happen? I'm glad
we're finally going back home. What is our new
house like? We're almost there?

I can't wait. Will any of my old friends be in school
with me? I wonder if I'll ever talk to Jenny again. I
don't even know where she is. I'll never, ever have
another friend as good as her.

*(Beat.)* I hope my new room is pink. *(Beat.)* Promise
we'll be safe in this new house?

---

### PRIVATE EYE NOTEBOOK

1. Circle clues about the *weather*.
2. Underline *facts* about the city or state.
3. Put a star next to *proper* nouns.
4. Why is this place famous or important?

NOTES: _____

_____

DOMINQUE: I am in

_____

# MATTHEW

*Matthew is talking to his father. The year is 1858.*

Pa, do you really think you'll find gold here? It's hard to breathe. Sure is pretty, though.

What are these mountains called? The Rockies? Boy, is it cold up here! Does anyone live here? Are there still Indians around here?

I can't wait to go home to Kansas.

## PRIVATE EYE NOTEBOOK

1. Circle clues about the *weather*.
2. Underline *facts* about the city or state.
3. Put a star next to *proper* nouns.
4. Why is this place famous or important?

NOTES: _____

_____

MATTEW: I am in

_____

# GRETA

*Greta is talking to a new neighbor.*

Hi! I'm Greta. Nice to meet you. This is my brother, Jacob, and my sister, Cissy. I have five other brothers and sisters. We're Mormons. That's a religion. Are you a Mormon, too? Oh. That's too bad.

Ow! Don't hit me, Jacob. I mean, that's fine. It's just that we won't see you at church.

Have you been to the lake yet? It's really salty. Saltier than the ocean! You can float on it. But don't swallow the water or get it in your eye. Hope you like the muffins we made! Welcome to town!

---

### PRIVATE EYE NOTEBOOK

1. Circle clues about the *weather*.
2. Underline *facts* about the city or state.
3. Put a star next to *proper* nouns.
4. Why is this place famous or important?

NOTES: _____

_____

GRETA: I am in

_____

---

# BENJI

*Benji is talking to his father.*

Why is this called the Garden State? It should be called the seashore state. That's a mouthful! There aren't so many gardens. I mean, Grandma has one, but she's the only person I know with a garden.

Why do people hate it here and make fun of it? It's not so bad. A girl came to school from Michigan, and she was sad her dad got a job here because she heard it was gross. But Michigan sounded the same as here. She played outside with her friends and did all the stuff we do. Only she didn't even have a beach or a boardwalk. She didn't even know what skee ball was! How can that be better? Let's not ever go to Michigan.

---

## PRIVATE EYE NOTEBOOK

1. Circle clues about the *weather*.
2. Underline *facts* about the city or state.
3. Put a star next to *proper* nouns.
4. Why is this place famous or important?

NOTES: _____

_____

BENJI: I am in

_____

---

# MADISON

*Madison is on vacation with her family—her mother, stepfather, and older sister.*

Oh my Goooooood, the Grand Canyon is HUGE! I feel like the air is burning my throat. I'm going to stand back; I feel like I'm going to fall in.

I like that the sand in the desert is sometimes pinkish and sometimes orange. It's pretty. There's so many cactuses.

How do you get down to the bottom? On a donkey? Ew!

---

## PRIVATE EYE NOTEBOOK

1. Circle clues about the *weather*.
2. Underline *facts* about the city or state.
3. Put a star next to *proper* nouns.
4. Why is this place famous or important?

NOTES: _____

_____

MADISON: I am in

_____

# HARRY

*Harry is doing a show-and-tell presentation at school.*

So this is my dad's guitar. Well, his favorite one. He's got lots. He's a guitar player. That's his job. He played at the Grand Ole Opry a bunch of times. And my great-grandma is in the Country Music Hall of Fame.

She is, too! You can go and see for yourself. My whole family has been in country music since as long as anyone can remember. When I grow up, I'm gonna play guitar and sing, too. And I'm gonna live here forever, except when I'm touring in a bus as a country music star. And I'm gonna have a thousand guitars in every color in the world!

## PRIVATE EYE NOTEBOOK

1. Circle clues about the *weather*.
2. Underline *facts* about the city or state.
3. Put a star next to *proper* nouns.
4. Why is this place famous or important?

NOTES: _____

_____

HARRY: I am in

_____

# EMMA

*Emma is talking to her best friend. The year is 1775.*

There's so much rushing around here. No one will tell me what's happening. But everybody seems nervous. That strange Mr. Franklin was here today. He seemed angry, but he gave me a candy and a kite. Told me not to fly it in a rainstorm, or I'd be hit by lightning!

Right now, there's a whole bunch of men in my dad's office. They're writing something.

I only heard them say one word: Liberty.

---

### PRIVATE EYE NOTEBOOK

1. Circle clues about the *weather*.
2. Underline *facts* about the city or state.
3. Put a star next to *proper* nouns.
4. Why is this place famous or important?

NOTES: _____

_____

EMMA: I am in

_____

# DON

*Don is talking to his family.*

Did the mountain just look like that? They made it look like that with dynamite? Cool!

So why are these presidents on Mount Rushmore? Why not other people?

I know that one of them is George Washington, but who are the others? Abraham Lincoln—oh! That's the one on the right! Who are the ones in the middle? Thomas Jefferson and Teddy Roosevelt? Oh—

Whoa! What was that? That was an eagle? Cool!

---

## PRIVATE EYE NOTEBOOK

1. Circle clues about the *weather*.
2. Underline *facts* about the city or state.
3. Put a star next to *proper* nouns.
4. Why is this place famous or important?

NOTES: _____

_____

DON: I am in

_____

---

# LUCY

*Lucy is talking to Paul Revere. It is April 19, 1775.*

Hey, mister? I understand that "the British are coming," but I'm trying to sleep. It's midnight, for Pete's sake.

OK, I'll promise to pass the message on to my dad. I think he's probably the only person in Lexington who didn't hear you.

You've got a really loud voice. Why are you telling everybody that the British are coming anyway? They've been here for years already.

Uh-oh. I'll wake up my dad now!

---

### PRIVATE EYE NOTEBOOK

1. Circle clues about the *weather*.
2. Underline *facts* about the city or state.
3. Put a star next to *proper* nouns.
4. Why is this place famous or important?

NOTES: _____

_____

LUCY: I am in

_____

# RUNNING BUFFALO

*Running Buffalo is talking to a white settler.*
*The year is 1889.*

This is Indian Territory. We set up many towns
here—Tulsa, Tishomingo, Muskogee. You can't
come and take it away from us. Why can't you just
leave us alone?

I'm tired of moving. I'm tired of running away. I'm
tired of being called a savage because I don't look
like you. Find some other place to live. I've gotten
used to living here. I'm not ever moving again.

## PRIVATE EYE NOTEBOOK

1. Circle clues about the *weather*.
2. Underline *facts* about the city or state.
3. Put a star next to *proper* nouns.
4. Why is this place famous or important?

NOTES: _____

_____

RUNNING BUFFALO: I am in

_____

# CHARLOTTE

*Charlotte is talking to her father. It is December 1866.*

Daddy, why did General Sherman burn down our house? And the whole town! I know we're on different sides of the war, but we didn't do anything to him. It doesn't seem fair. I wish you woulda let me go back for my baby doll. She burned in the fire for sure! Poor baby. I bet she thought I didn't love her. But I did!

I'm gonna miss Bessie, too. I know it was good for us to set her free so she wouldn't have to be a slave. But I liked the way she sang me to sleep. Even if we build a whole new house, I don't know if it'll feel like home to me.

---

## PRIVATE EYE NOTEBOOK

1. Circle clues about the *weather*.
2. Underline *facts* about the city or state.
3. Put a star next to *proper* nouns.
4. Why is this place famous or important?

NOTES: _____

_____

CHARLOTTE: I am in

_____

# SAM

*Sam is talking to a hotel worker and his sister, Sarah.*

Are you the room service guy? Do you have my hot fudge sundae? Chocolate-chip cookies? Macaroni and cheese? Milk? OK, good. Bring it in.

Can I ask you a question before you go? What do kids do here? My parents are gambling downstairs, and my sister just wants to watch videos. But this isn't really fun to me.

There's a pool? *(Yelling.)* Sarah, get off the phone! I want to go swimming!

Thanks, mister!

---

## PRIVATE EYE NOTEBOOK

1. Circle clues about the *weather*.
2. Underline *facts* about the city or state.
3. Put a star next to *proper* nouns.
4. Why is this place famous or important?

NOTES: _____

_____

SAM: I am in

_____

# MILEY

*Miley is wearing a long dress and cap. She is talking to a crowd of people, pretending she is from Colonial times.*

Welcome to Colonial World! My name is Cordelia. I am the daughter of Emily and James Hatten. We are glassmakers. Over there is my brother. He is in the stocks because he stole candy from Mister Gardner's general store. He's not very smart, and sometimes I pretend he's not really my brother.

Come with me, and we'll go to my parent's workshop. It's very hot in there. It's dangerous, too, so don't touch anything. I'm too young to do glassblowing, and my brother can't concentrate. But it's really fun to watch. Follow me!

---

**PRIVATE EYE NOTEBOOK**

1. Circle clues about the *weather*.
2. Underline *facts* about the city or state.
3. Put a star next to *proper* nouns.
4. Why is this place famous or important?

NOTES: _____

_____

MILEY: I am in

_____

# JASON

*Jason is talking to his family.*

This was a jail? I can see why. Even if you escaped from the island, you'd have to swim for, like, a whole day to get to land. I bet the water's cold, too.

Some guys might have escaped? They dug holes in the wall with spoons? Wow that must have taken a long, long time!

No one lives here on Alcatraz now, right? Dad, why don't we live here? Then we could all get our own room!

---

## PRIVATE EYE NOTEBOOK

1. Circle clues about the *weather*.
2. Underline *facts* about the city or state.
3. Put a star next to *proper* nouns.
4. Why is this place famous or important?

NOTES: _____

_____

JASON: I am in

_____

# KATE

*Kate is talking to her best friend, Rosie.*

Rosie, I'm having a party this weekend during the Derby. While my dad is watching the horse race, my mom said I can have a tea party. You have to wear a hat, though. A big hat. I'm going to make one. So you can do that, too, if you want.

Oh! I forgot the best part! I'm going to get my own pony! And we can ride him that day, too!

So, will you come?

## PRIVATE EYE NOTEBOOK

1. Circle clues about the *weather*.
2. Underline *facts* about the city or state.
3. Put a star next to *proper* nouns.
4. Why is this place famous or important?

NOTES: _____

_____

KATE: I am in

_____

# ANSWERS!

| | |
|---|---|
| Leah is in | Los Angeles, California |
| Iain is in | Washington D.C. |
| Jodie is in | Anchorage, Alaska |
| Rich is in | Detroit, Michigan |
| Laila is in | Honolulu, Hawaii |
| Christian is in | Laredo, Texas |
| Jazmeen is in | New York, New York |
| Thomas is in | Nantucket, Massachusetts |
| Iris is in | Fort Lauderdale, Florida |
| Jay is in | Chicago, Illinois |
| Dominique is in | New Orleans, Louisiana |
| Matthew is in | Denver, Colorado |
| Greta is in | Salt Lake City, Utah |
| Benji is in | Point Pleasant, New Jersey |
| Madison is in | Flagstaff, Arizona |
| Harry is in | Nashville, Tennessee |
| Emma is in | Philadelphia, Pennsylvania |
| Don is in | Keystone, South Dakota |
| Lucy is in | Boston, Massachusetts |
| Running Buffalo is in | Tahlequah, Oklahoma |
| Charlotte is in | Atlanta, Georgia |

| | |
|---|---|
| Sam is in | Las Vegas, Nevada |
| Miley is in | Williamsburg, Virginia |
| Jason is in | San Francisco Bay, California |
| Kate is in | Louisville, Kentucky |

# Part 3
# FAR: FOREIGN COUNTRIES

In this section, each character is in
a place outside the United States.
See what you can find out about each place.

Where is this boy? Draw the place around him.

# MICKEY

*Mickey is talking to his father.*

I don't like camels. That was the bumpiest ride I ever took! My camel is mean and spits a lot. I thought this would be—

Whoa. That's awesome! They're huge! When I saw the pyramids in pictures, I never thought they'd be SO BIG!

People made them? Without cranes? No way. That's impossible! How did they get the stones so high? And each stone is bigger that me, so they're way heavy. This place is awesome! Can we see some mummies?

---

## ATLAS
### *Welcome to . . .* CAIRO, EGYPT!

North, south, east, or west? _____

Near water? _____

Weather?_____

Historical places? _____

Famous for? _____

Traditions? _____

---

# OLIVIA

*Olivia is talking to her mother.*

Mom? Mom? That guy is trying to talk to you, I think. I think you're not supposed to touch the statue. He's nodding his head! I'm right! I can understand another language, Mom!

How much longer do we have to look at art? It's very pretty, but I'm hungry. Can we go to the piazza so all the birds can land on me again? That was fun. Then we can go get another gelato! This time I want, ummm, cherry gelato! Please?

---

## ATLAS
### *Welcome to . . . ROME, ITALY!*

North, south, east, or west? _____

Near water? _____

Weather?_____

Historical places? _____

Famous for? _____

Traditions? _____

---

# RAFE

*Rafe is talking to an American girl.*

My father is a race-car driver. He is! Once a year, they clear out all the streets in town, and there's a big race. Only real race-car drivers can do it, silly. Regular people don't know how to do it.

Everyone here is very rich. People come here to gamble, too. They don't care if they lose money because they're rich. I'm not bragging! It's true!

---

## ATLAS

*Welcome to . . .* MONTE CARLO, MONACO!

North, south, east, or west? _____

Near water? _____

Weather?_____

Historical places? _____

Famous for? _____

Traditions? _____

# JENNA

*Jenna is talking to her mother. They are
inside a palace.*

People used to live here? Is this really all gold? They
must have been pretty people, too, because there are
lots of mirrors. Does anyone live here now? No?
Probably because they can't afford it.

Mom, is what that tour guide said true? That the
men wore high heels with jewels, and the women
wore wigs, and sometimes rats lived in the wigs, and
the king and queen had their heads chopped off?
Why did they get their heads chopped off?

Ooooh. They lived here and had lots of food and
gold, and the people outside were starving. I guess
they weren't very nice. Or clean. But it sure is pretty.

---

## ATLAS
### *Welcome to . . .* VERSAILLES, FRANCE!

North, south, east, or west? _____

Near water? _____

Weather?_____

Historical places? _____

Famous for? _____

Traditions? _____

---

# BRYAN

*Bryan is talking to a boy he just met.*

You and your dad live here? In the Tower? You get locked in at night? That's so cool! How come you get to live here? What's a Beefeater? Wow. So do they still hold people prisoner here for trying to kill the queen? Oh. Well, it's still cool. You don't have to live in a cell, do you?

Can you try on the suits of armor when no one's looking? Oh. Is it creepy here at night? That's so cool!

---

## ATLAS
### *Welcome to . . .* LONDON, ENGLAND!

North, south, east, or west? _____

Near water? _____

Weather?_____

Historical places? _____

Famous for? _____

Traditions? _____

---

# GWEN

*Gwen is talking to her father.*

Do you think we'll see lions? How about giraffes? How about zebras? Yes, I'll be quiet when we go out. Do you think we'll see monkeys? Oh, I love monkeys. They're so cute! Can I feed the animals? No?

I know they're wild animals. I'll be careful. I promise I'll be quiet, and I won't feed them. Even if they're very cute. Why is this called a safari? Because we're so-far-i from home? That was a good joke, wasn't it?

---

## ATLAS
*Welcome to . . . KENYA!*

North, south, east, or west? _____

Near water? _____

Weather?_____

Historical places? _____

Famous for? _____

Traditions? _____

# LYLE

*Lyle is talking to a tour guide.*

So why didn't the white people like the black people? No reason? So were black people slaves? Just poor. And they couldn't vote. And they were killed and put in jail. Wow.

Well, I think black people and white people should get along, and that black people should be allowed to be rich and in charge, too. I think people should go to jail for being bad, not for the color of their skin.

---

## ATLAS
### Welcome to . . . SOUTH AFRICA!

North, south, east, or west? _____

Near water? _____

Weather?_____

Historical places? _____

Famous for? _____

Traditions? _____

# MARTA

*Marta is talking to her mother.*

There are so many tulips here! Tulips are my favorite flower now. I love them.

What language are people speaking? Dutch? Is the Little Dutch Boy from here? The one who put his finger in the dike to stop the town from flooding? Did that really happen?

If everyone here used to wear clogs like that Dutch boy, this must have been a very noisy place to live. Dutch people from long ago must have had terrible headaches.

---

## ATLAS
*Welcome to . . .* AMSTERDAM, HOLLAND!

North, south, east, or west? _____

Near water? _____

Weather? _____

Historical places? _____

Famous for? _____

Traditions? _____

---

# JEFF

*Jeff is talking to his father.*

This must be the brightest place in the world! There are so many signs that light up! How can people think?

There are cartoons and video games everywhere. Do a lot of kids live here? There's Digimon and Yu-Gi-Oh! and Hello Kitty on everything!

Can we see sumo wrestlers tomorrow, Dad? You promised we could. Why do those fat guys wear diapers?

Can we get some real food tonight? I don't want any sushi. I want a hot dog.

---

## ATLAS
### *Welcome to . . . TOKYO, JAPAN!*

North, south, east, or west? _____

Near water? _____

Weather?_____

Historical places? _____

Famous for? _____

Traditions? _____

---

# PADMA

*Padma is talking to her grandmother.*

Grandma, why are there so many little children in the street who chase after us when we get in the car? They're poor? That's sad.

What was that big white building called that we visited? The Taj Mahal? They should let the poor children live there. There's lots of room.

I think it's good that we don't eat cows. Cows have such gentle, sad eyes; I don't know why people would want to eat them!

---

## ATLAS
*Welcome to . . . INDIA!*

North, south, east, or west? _____

Near water? _____

Weather?_____

Historical places? _____

Famous for? _____

Traditions? _____

---

# IVAN

*Ivan is talking to his mother.*

Why are all the letters here funny? They have different letters? That must be hard to learn! Do you know the letters, Mom? You forget?

Why is that building called a gremlin? The Kremlin? I like the name gremlin better.

If Communism is about sharing with other people, how come people don't like it? You always tell me to share.

Everybody here has a long name. Mister Blabby-din-sky. Misses Grouchy-itch. Writing your name at the top of your paper in school must make your hand sore!

---

## ATLAS
### *Welcome to . . . MOSCOW, RUSSIA!*

North, south, east, or west? _____

Near water? _____

Weather?_____

Historical places? _____

Famous for? _____

Traditions? _____

# BLAIR

*Blair is talking to her father.*

Did you know about this? This is the best place in the world! This must be where Barbie lives. The sand is pink!!! Pink sand! Is this real, or did someone make it like this? We have to move here. We have to! This is where I want to live forever. You like the beach. We can live in our hotel room so we can see the ocean all the time.

We can scuba dive and snorkel all day! You don't have to work. We can just be on vacation all the time! Come on, Dad. Please? This is my favorite place in the world!

---

## ATLAS
### *Welcome to . . .* BERMUDA!

North, south, east, or west? _____

Near water? _____

Weather?_____

Historical places? _____

Famous for? _____

Traditions? _____

# HUGH

*Hugh is talking to another boy his age.*

G'day! You've never been here before? There are so many awesome things to do here! You can go to the zoo and see our koalas, kangaroos, dingos, wombats, and wallabies. Or you can surf—my dad is teaching me how!

Listen, mate we're having some shrimp and kebobs on the barbie later on. You can come over, and we'll drink sarsaparilla. I reckon we'll have a ripping good time!

---

## ATLAS
*Welcome to . . .* SYDNEY, AUSTRALIA!

North, south, east, or west? _____

Near water? _____

Weather?_____

Historical places? _____

Famous for? _____

Traditions? _____

---

# URSULA

*Ursula is talking to an American boy.*

You don't believe in elves? Or fairies? Or dwarfs?
Or gnomes? Why not? I do! Everyone I know
believes in magic folks. We're even careful not to
make roads where we might disturb their homes!
Well, can you imagine how awful that would be?
One day you're sitting peacefully in your house having some hot cocoa, and the next moment a bull-
dozer is crushing your sofa!

Oh, you really must believe. There is a family of
fairies that lives near my house. They get very hurt
and angry when people aren't nice to them. In fact,
Triven, a boy fairy, is just about to bite your foot!
I think you'd better apologize to him now!

---

## ATLAS
*Welcome to . . . ICELAND!*

North, south, east, or west? _____

Near water? _____

Weather?_____

Historical places? _____

Famous for? _____

Traditions? _____

---

# TONY

*Tony is talking to his mother.*

Mom, help! I'm getting smushed! This is the busiest place I've ever been in my life!

Oh, look! There's an acrobat over there! I hope we see a snake charmer.

Why do people keep yelling? At home, no one yells at you in the grocery store. This is the craziest market in the world!

That guy is selling carpets—do you think they can fly?

---

## ATLAS
*Welcome to . . .* MARRAKESH, MOROCCO!

North, south, east, or west? _____

Near water? _____

Weather?_____

Historical places? _____

Famous for? _____

Traditions? _____

---

# DANIELLE

*Danielle is talking to an elevator operator.*

*Bonjour!* So this is the Eiffel Tower. It's pretty big! The elevator to the top is so loud! Why don't they get a new one?

All my mom wants to do here is go shopping. I think the lights here are pretty. I haven't seen any schoolgirls who look like Madeline yet. That used to be my favorite book.

This is the top? It's windy!

---

## ATLAS
### *Welcome to . . .* PARIS, FRANCE!

North, south, east, or west? _____

Near water? _____

Weather?_____

Historical places? _____

Famous for? _____

Traditions? _____

# LIAM

*Liam is talking to his mother.*

There are too many tourists here! Maybe we have too many festivals. There's the theater festival when the jugglers, magicians, singers, and dancers are all over the streets. Then there's my favorite, the Fire Festival—

It's just too popular here, Mum! Maybe we should only let people visit if they eat haggis. I bet a lot of people would leave if we told them they had to eat sheep's guts!

---

## ATLAS
### *Welcome to . . .* EDINBURGH, SCOTLAND!

North, south, east, or west? _____

Near water? _____

Weather? _____

Historical places? _____

Famous for? _____

Traditions? _____

---

# ALLISON

*Allison is talking to her family.*

This is a very tricky place. Yesterday, a lady hollered at me for putting a book on the floor.

Today, when I went to get a bug out of Sabrina's hair, a man said, "Never touch the head!"

And just this minute, a monkey stole my mango! I thought monkeys were sweet!

This is a very confusing vacation!

---

**ATLAS**

*Welcome to . . .* THAILAND!

North, south, east, or west? _____

Near water? _____

Weather?_____

Historical places? _____

Famous for? _____

Traditions? _____

# THEO

*Theo is talking to his older brother.*

Hey, Marcus, how come everyone's drinking beer and eating sauerkraut? Beer smells bad and sauerkraut looks like barf.

I know it's Oktoberfest. That's a supposed to be big party, right? Well, how come no one does anything but eat and drink? What's so fun about that?

Maybe I would understand it if they were eating meatballs and drinking milkshakes. Now that would seem like a party to me!

---

## ATLAS
*Welcome to . . . MUNICH, GERMANY!*

North, south, east, or west? _____

Near water? _____

Weather? _____

Historical places? _____

Famous for? _____

Traditions? _____

---

# MATILDA

*Matilda is talking to a tourist.*

In your country, you only speak one language?
I speak three languages, and I'm only seven!
English, German, and French. We have three
national languages here. Since my mom owns this
inn, it's important to be able to talk to everyone.

Oh, have you been skiing yet? The Alps are the best
place to ski in the world! I like to go up to the top of
a mountain and scream. It's fun! You should try it.

## ATLAS
### Welcome to . . . SWITZERLAND!

North, south, east, or west? _____

Near water? _____

Weather?_____

Historical places? _____

Famous for? _____

Traditions? _____

# ANABAR

*Anabar is talking to a cameraman.*

It does get lonely sometimes. We're the only people who live here. Sometimes we come across another tribe, but most of the time, it's just us and the animals. Walking across the tundra.

You get used to the cold. I remember when I was a little boy, I thought the snow was so bright sometimes. Now it doesn't bother me anymore. In fact, I like it. There are times when it's dark here for months and months. That's the time when it gets the loneliest.

---

### ATLAS
*Welcome to . . .* SIBERIA!

North, south, east, or west? _____

Near water? _____

Weather?_____

Historical places? _____

Famous for? _____

Traditions? _____

---

# LUIZA

*Luiza is talking to her mother.*

Please, please may I go to carnival? It's not dangerous!

Mama . . . if I can't go to carnival . . . can I have a party here with my friends? If you let me have a party, I promise I'll stop asking to go.

Thank you, thank you! Can I wear a bikini and a big, feathered hat and play drums and shimmy-shake like the carnival girls? Please, Mama? I want this party to be just like the real thing!

---

## ATLAS
*Welcome to . . .* RIO DE JANEIRO, BRAZIL!

North, south, east, or west? _____

Near water? _____

Weather?_____

Historical places? _____

Famous for? _____

Traditions? _____

---

# HAKIM

*Hakim is talking to a soldier.*

I used to live in Baghdad, but now I live here. I liked living in the city, but it got to be too dangerous because of the war. Here we don't have electricity. There's not really a school, so my dad brings me books sometimes. We might move to Iran. I'm not sure when, though.

You don't like the sand? I have a book about this girl who has a garden, which I think is very peculiar. I've never seen one! And I can't imagine spending all day planting flowers. But it must be nice.

---

### ATLAS
#### *Welcome to . . . IRAQ!*

North, south, east, or west? _____

Near water? _____

Weather?_____

Historical places? _____

Famous for? _____

Traditions? _____

---

# MALLIKA

*Mallika is talking to a new girl in school.*

This is one of the richest countries in the world. And it's not very big, either! We just finished building the tallest hotel in the world. In fact, the government had to build a new island, just for the hotel!

When I'm twenty-one, I'm going to marry this boy Raj my parents picked for me. That's the only thing about living here that I'm not so crazy about. Raj has cooties!

---

## ATLAS
*Welcome to . . . DUBAI!*

North, south, east, or west? _____

Near water? _____

Weather?_____

Historical places? _____

Famous for? _____

Traditions? _____

---

# IGOR

*Igor is talking to a girl in his class.*

I've never told this to you before, but . . . I'm a
vampire. I am! I'm related to Dracula. Am, too!
You better believe me, or I'll bite your neck,
Anastasia. I will! Don't dare me!

How do you know I'm not a vampire? I live in the
castle on the hill. I do!

No one listens to me.

---

## ATLAS
*Welcome to . . .* TRANSYLVANIA, HUNGARY!

North, south, east, or west? _____

Near water? _____

Weather?_____

Historical places? _____

Famous for? _____

Traditions? _____

---

# CHRISTINA

*Christina is talking to an American reporter.*

In other countries, people have to pay to go to the doctor. Not here. Everyone gets to go to the doctor, no matter how much money they have. Being healthy is important, and everyone deserves to feel good.

Not everyone here has blonde hair and blue eyes. I don't know why people think that! It's also not cold all the time.

My friends and I think a lot about the environment. We want the earth to be around forever!

---

**ATLAS**
*Welcome to . . . SWEDEN!*

North, south, east, or west? _____

Near water? _____

Weather?_____

Historical places? _____

Famous for? _____

Traditions? _____

---

# JOEL

*Joel is talking to his father.*

Dad, there's a new Palestinian boy at my school. He seems nice. Why are we fighting with them? Is it just because of land?

He's not Jewish? He's Muslim? Well, there's a Catholic boy in school, too. Are we fighting with him, too? It's very confusing to me. I don't think I want to fight with anyone.

## ATLAS
### *Welcome to . . . CAIRO, EGYPT!*

North, south, east, or west? _____

Near water? _____

Weather? _____

Historical places? _____

Famous for? _____

Traditions? _____

# ALICE

*Alice is talking to a film crew.*

I am the first kid ever to come here. Before, only grown-up scientists visited. People can't really live here. Even though it's in the south, it's not warm. It's very, very, very, very, very cold!

You'll see lots of penguins and seals here. They like ice and snow. But did you know that the ice is melting? Sometimes the animals get lost at sea. That's why I came here. I want to save the animals in the South Pole!

---

## ATLAS
### Welcome to . . . ANTARCTICA!

North, south, east, or west? _____

Near water? _____

Weather?_____

Historical places? _____

Famous for? _____

Traditions? _____

---

# NIKO

*Niko is talking to Zeus, the king of the gods.*
*The year is 130 BC.*

Zeus, my father told me to sacrifice a lamb to the
gods so we will have a good harvest this year, but . . .
I like lambs. They're just babies. I don't want to kill
any of them. Will you be angry if I disobey my
father? It just doesn't seem fair!

Zeus, I promise to do all of my chores for the rest of
my life as long as I don't have to sacrifice a lamb
this year.

---

## ATLAS
### *Welcome to . . . CAIRO, EGYPT!*

North, south, east, or west? _____

Near water? _____

Weather?_____

Historical places? _____

Famous for? _____

Traditions? _____

---

# ADRIANA

*Adriana is talking to a tourist.*

*Bueños tardes!* Would you like a taco? I promise you, you have never had a taco as good as the ones my *madre* makes. She grows the jalepeños peppers in our backyard.

I am not too young to work! My whole family works here. My brother, Diego, will play guitar for you. Here, wear a sombrero. It will keep you cool in the hot sun.

Oh, I have loads of energy! My *padre* calls me his little jumping bean. Señor, prepare yourself for a food fiesta!

---

## ATLAS
### *Welcome to . . . MEXICO!*

North, south, east, or west? _____

Near water? _____

Weather?_____

Historical places? _____

Famous for? _____

Traditions? _____

# Part 4
# FAR: IMAGINARY AND FAR-OUT PLACES

In this section, each character is in a place that's magical and not of this world. Guess where you are from the list on the next page! Answers are on page 115. Write your own story about each place in the Travel Journal.

Where is this girl? Draw the place around her.

Match a place from the list
below to each monologue.

Mars                 Santa's workshop

Oz                   Neverland

Wonderland           Candy Land

Hogwarts             Mount Olympus

Sesame Street        The End of the Rainbow

Dragon's lair        Heaven

# JERRY

Excuse me! I'm lost. Can anyone help me?

I'm the tallest person in the room! That's never happened before.

It sure is busy here. You work very hard! Hey, these are toys! Wow, I love that train set!

Get to work? But I'm not from here, mister. I don't know how to build a gingerbread house! Can you tell me the way to Connecticut?

## GUESS!

Jerry is talking to _____.

Jerry is in _____.

---

### TRAVEL JOURNAL

Be an explorer. Imagine you are in this place. What is it like? _____

_____

_____

---

# CARRIE

I'm so nervous! Are we supposed to know anything? I don't know anything. My parents are Muggles. This robe is itching me!

Do you know what house you want to be in? I'm so excited to sit down to dinner at the Great Hall—I'm going to eat absolutely everything!

Whoa! The stairs are moving! Oh, I don't want to get lost on my very first day! Help!

## GUESS!

Carrie is talking to _____.

Carrie is at _____.

---

### TRAVEL JOURNAL

Be an explorer. Imagine you are in this place.
What is it like? _____

_____

_____

---

# STAN

I caught you! Where is it? You know what. The pot of gold! It's supposed to be right here. Where did you hide it?

You spent it? On what? Video games? I don't believe you. You're trying to trick me! It won't work. I'm very smart. I bet you hid your pot of gold in the trees over here. *(Looks away.)*

*(Looks back to where the man was standing.)* Hey, where did you go?

## GUESS!

Stan is talking to _____.

Stan is at _____.

---

### TRAVEL JOURNAL

Be an explorer. Imagine you are in this place. What is it like? _____

_____

_____

# ELLEN

I was just trying to throw something away. I didn't know you lived in that trash can! Well, why would anyone live in the garbage? It's dirty and smelly—you like that?

Well, that's very unusual. Hey—did you see that? That bird must be seven feet tall! This is some weird street. In the past five minutes, I've seen a huge bird, a guy who lives in the trash, and a little red thing that couldn't stop laughing.

What a day this has been!

## GUESS!

Ellen is talking to _____.

Ellen is on _____.

---

### TRAVEL JOURNAL

Be an explorer. Imagine you are in this place.
What is it like? _____

_____

_____

# DAMIAN

Where are you going? I'm trying to ask you a question! You don't need to be scared of me. I never saw a lion who was scared before.

Can you tell me where to get a root beer around here? I'm thirsty.

Fine. I'll ask the Wizard. Where is he?

That doesn't make sense. I don't want to walk for miles and miles to ask him to grant me a root beer. I'm thirsty now! I'll walk all the way down this path when monkeys fly! Oh. I guess I'd better start walking.

## GUESS!

Damian is talking to _____.

Damian is in _____.

---

### TRAVEL JOURNAL

Be an explorer. Imagine you are in this place.
What is it like? _____

_____

_____

# LILLY

What's happening to me? I feel funny. *(Screams.)* There's something on my back! Help! It's big!

Oh. It's my wings? Why do I need wings? I seem to be able to just float on clouds.

They're just for show? Well, they are pretty.

Um, I don't want to complain, but . . . my halo is tight. It's giving me a headache. Could you loosen it?

Whew! Thanks! I feel much better now.

## GUESS!

Lilly is talking to _____.

Lilly is in _____.

---

### TRAVEL JOURNAL

Be an explorer. Imagine you are in this place.
What is it like? _____

_____

_____

# PETE

Take me to your leader! I didn't think anyone actually lived here.

May I ask you a question? I hope you don't think I'm rude. Why are your noses on your necks? And why do you have seven lips?

You think I look strange? Well, at least I don't have three butts!

**GUESS!**

Pete is talking to _____.

Pete is on _____.

---

### TRAVEL JOURNAL

Be an explorer. Imagine you are in this place. What is it like? _____

_____

_____

---

# MARY

Drink this. Eat this. This is the bossiest place on earth! I like to do what I want, when I want!

Off with your head, madame! You see, I am the Queen of Smarts! Let's play a game of wits. Number one: Where do you live? Wrong! You live at home. Number two: Where did you come from? Wrong again! You came from your mother's stomach! Number three: Where do you get bananas? Wrong once more. You get bananas from the top of the refrigerator.

Off with her head!

## GUESS!

Mary is talking to _____.

Mary is in _____.

---

### TRAVEL JOURNAL

Be an explorer. Imagine you are in this place. What is it like? _____

_____

_____

---

# SETH

Oh, boy. I never, ever thought I'd say this! I wish I had some . . . broccoli.

Today I had candy canes for breakfast with Lord Licorice. Then I went swimming in Chocolate Swamp.

*(Sighs.)* OK, fine. I'll sit down and eat my candy canes, Gramma. What's for dinner? Awwwww, not cookies again!

## GUESS!

Seth is talking to _____.

Seth is in _____.

---

### TRAVEL JOURNAL

Be an explorer. Imagine you are in this place. What is it like? _____

_____

_____

# BELL

You are the silliest boy alive. What makes you think I loooooove you? Yuck!

You and the Lost Boys never take a bath or brush your teeth. I am glad that I can fly away when you talk about hhhhhow hhhhungry you are after hhh-hunting hhhhares. Your breath smells awful, you rotten little boy!

## GUESS!

Bell is talking to _____.

Bell is in _____.

---

### TRAVEL JOURNAL

Be an explorer. Imagine you are in this place.
What is it like? _____

_____

_____

---

# DRACO

Whoops! Sorry. Don't worry. You're hair will grow back. It's only burned a little. Whenever I eat spicy food—zoom! Fire rushes out of my mouth.

You've come to slay me? Look, I'm a little sleepy. Why don't you come back later and we'll fight, I'll kill you, blah, blah, blah. Give me about an hour to rest up. OK?

**GUESS!**

Draco is talking to _____.

Draco is in _____.

---

### TRAVEL JOURNAL

Be an explorer. Imagine you are in this place.
What is it like? _____

_____

_____

# STEPHI

Hello. I'm here to complain. To Apollo, the sun god. Oh, you're his dad. Can I tell you my problem?

It's summer. In the summer, I go swimming. But this summer the sun hasn't been out at all. It's done nothing but rain! I hate it! What's going on?

Apollo is depressed? He's just sitting in his room? Well, you're the king of the gods. Why don't you do something to cheer him up? It would make me really happy.

**GUESS!**

Stephi is talking to _____.

Stephi is on _____.

---

**TRAVEL JOURNAL**

Be an explorer. Imagine you are in this place. What is it like? _____

_____

_____

# ANSWERS!

| | |
|---|---|
| Jerry is talking to | an elf. |
| Jerry is in | Santa's workshop. |
| | |
| Carrie is talking to | another new student. |
| Carrie is at | Hogwarts. |
| | |
| Stan is talking to | a leprechaun. |
| Stan is at | the end of the rainbow. |
| | |
| Ellen is talking to | Oscar the Grouch. |
| Ellen is on | Sesame Street. |
| | |
| Damian is talking to | the Cowardly Lion. |
| Damian is in | Oz. |
| | |
| Lilly is talking to | an angel. |
| Lilly is in | Heaven. |
| | |
| Pete is talking to | an alien. |
| Pete is on | Mars. |
| | |
| Mary is talking to | the Queen of Hearts. |
| Mary is in | Wonderland. |
| | |
| Seth is talking to | Gramma Nutt. |
| Seth is in | Candy Land. |
| Bell is talking to | Peter Pan. |

Bell is in             Neverland.

Draco is talking to    a prince or a knight.
Draco is in            a dragon's lair.

Stephi is talking to   Zeus.
Stephi is on           Mount Olympus.

## ABOUT THE AUTHOR

**Kristen Dabrowski** is an actress, writer, acting teacher, and director. The actor's life has taken her all over the United States and England. Her other books, published by Smith and Kraus, include *My First Monologue Book; 111 Monologues for Middle School Actors; The Ultimate Audition Book for Teens 3, 11,* and *12; 20 Ten-Minute Plays for Teens;* the Teens Speak series; and the educational 10+ play series (six books, including two volumes for kids). Currently, she lives in the world's smallest apartment in New York City. You can contact the author at monologuemadness @yahoo.com.